Unidentified Laughing Objects

SpongeBob's
Book of
Space-y Jokes

Stephen Hillenburg

Based on the TV series *SpongeBob SquarePants*™ created by Stephen Hillenburg as seen on Nickelodeon™

SIMON SPOTLIGHT

An imprint of Simon & Schuster Children's Publishing Division
1230 Avenue of the Americas, New York, New York 10020
© 2011 Viacom International Inc. All rights reserved. NICKELODEON,
SpongeBob SquarePants, and all related titles, logos, and characters
are trademarks of Viacom International Inc.
Created by Stephen Hillenburg.
All rights reserved, including the right of reproduction in whole
or in part in any form.
SIMON SPOTLIGHT and colophon are registered trademarks
of Simon & Schuster, Inc.
For information about special discounts for bulk purchases,
please contact Simon & Schuster Special Sales at 1-866-506-1949
or business@simonandschuster.com.
Manufactured in the United States of America 0711 OFF
First Edition
2 4 6 8 10 9 7 5 3 1
ISBN 978-1-4424-3937-5

SpongeBob SquarePants™

Unidentified Laughing Objects

SpongeBob's
Book of
Space-y Jokes

by Rebecca McCarthy

Simon Spotlight/Nickelodeon

New York   London   Toronto   Sydney

SpongeBob knocked on the door of Sandy's treedome, hoping she would want to go out and play. He knocked and knocked, but there was no answer.

"Oh," SpongeBob groaned. "All I want to do is hang out with my friends today, but no one seems to be home! I've gone to Patrick's, Squidward's, the Krusty Krab, and even Mrs. Puff's driving school! Where can everyone be?"

Just then a giant spaceship rose out of the ground by the treedome. It was much larger than the rocket Sandy usually used to fly to the moon. SpongeBob couldn't believe his eyes.

"Wow!" SpongeBob exclaimed. "A new rocket! Sandy must be up to something big!"

"This ain't no rocket, SpongeBob," came Sandy's

voice from a window up top. "It's a spaceship! I'm going to explore outer space."

"You . . . you mean you're not just going on one of your usual trips to the moon to collect moon rocks? You're really going to go . . . even farther?" SpongeBob asked.

"That's right, little square dude!" Sandy said excitedly.

SpongeBob stared at the spaceship, then suddenly burst out, "Can I come? Oh please, please, please, can I come too?" He dropped to his knees and begged. Sandy smiled, shut the window and trotted down to the bottom of the ship. She opened the hatch and motioned for him to enter.

"Well, sure, friend," she said. "It's a long trip up into outer space, and I could use the company. By the time we get there, why, you and I will be tighter than sardines in a can!"

"Hooray!" SpongeBob shouted. "Thank you, Sandy!"

Soon the spaceship blasted off, and after helping Sandy check that everything was okay, they decided to pass the time by telling jokes.

All of a sudden they heard a snickering sound coming from a cabinet under the control panel.

Heh-heh-heh, heh-heh-heh . . .

"What can that be?" SpongeBob asked. "We checked everything."

"I don't know," Sandy replied, "but I'm sure gonna find out."

She opened the door to the cabinet, and out rolled . . . Patrick Star!

"Patrick, what in tarnation are you doin' here?" Sandy asked, surprised.

"Uh, I saw your spaceship this morning and thought it looked like a swell place to take a nap," Patrick said.

"So that's why you weren't home today!" SpongeBob said, snapping his fingers.

Sandy sighed. "Well, you're here now."

"Yeah, and I have a joke," Patrick said.

But before he could tell his joke, another voice was heard from the air vent. "I've got one too!"

SpongeBob opened the vent and found Mrs. Puff stuffed inside. She smiled

sheepishly and held out her arms. Patrick, SpongeBob, and Sandy pulled her into the control room.

"You too?" Sandy exclaimed.

"Oh, yes," explained Mrs. Puff. "I've always wanted to learn how to drive a spaceship. I hope you'll forgive me for stowing away. I do have a few jokes I can tell."

"Well, the more, the merrier!" Sandy said.

"Ah, I'm glad to hear ya say that, lassie," said a raspy voice coming from up high. Everyone looked up to see Mr. Krabs climbing down from the top shelf. Behind him came his daughter, Pearl.

SpongeBob gasped, "So THAT'S where you've been! I was wondering why the Krusty Krab was closed today."

"The Krusty Krab was closed?" Mr. Krabs asked, surprised. "But I left Squidward in charge to run me business for the day so I could search for space treasure."

"Uh, actually, Mr. Krabs . . . ," said Squidward, wiggling out of a storage closet.

"Squidward!" Mr. Krabs shouted, "What are you doing here?"

"Well, there were no customers, so I figured it would be okay if I took off for a while," Squidward replied. "What are you doing here?"

"Now, now, everyone," Sandy said calmly. "It's all right. This new spaceship has plenty of room for all of you. Welcome aboard!"

"Uh . . . ahem . . ." A small voice cleared its throat.

Everyone looked down, just as Plankton slithered out from behind a wall panel. Mr. Krabs glared at him. "Oh no, Krabs, I'm not here to steal your secret formula.

I've just always wanted to see what it would be like to float in space," he said.

Sandy chuckled, slapped her knee, and said, "Well, I'll be a monkey's aunt! As the captain of this ship, I say, sure y'all can join us for the ride—as long as you provide us with some space laughs!"

With that, SpongeBob, Patrick, Squidward, Mr. Krabs, Pearl, Mrs. Puff, and Plankton fastened their seat belts, sat back, and looked up while they rose through the sea, into the air, as high as the moon, and beyond!

What is Mr. Krabs's favorite thing about living on Earth?

The free trip around the sun!

When do astronauts have their afternoon meal?

At launch time!

What dance steps can cows
do in outer space?

The mooooooon walk!

What's the best way to serve a cup of tea in outer space?

On flying saucers!

What kind of star doesn't live in outer space?

Patrick Star!

What kind of star wears sunglasses?

A movie star!

What do you call a bear from the north side of the sun?

A solar polar!

Did you hear about the new restaurant on the moon?

Yes, the food is excellent, but there's no atmosphere!

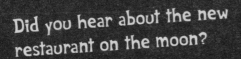

What do you call a loony spaceman?

An astro-nut!

How did Squidward greet a three-headed alien?

Hello! Hello! Hello!

Why don't astronauts get hungry after being blasted into space?

Because they've just had a big launch.

What do you call an alien starship that drips water?

A crying saucer!

Why don't astronauts keep their jobs very long?

Because as soon as they start they get fired!

How does the solar system hold up its pants?

With an asteroid belt!

What did the metric alien say to Gary?

"Take me to your liter!"

What do you call a crazy man on the moon?

A lunar-tic!

What do space cowboys use
on their horses?

Saddle-lites!

What do you call a sick
extraterrestrial?

An ailin' alien!

Why didn't the Dog Star laugh at the joke?

Because it was Sirius!

If one out of ten meteorites hit a planet, what do we call the other nine?

Meteor-wrongs!

What kind of songs do the planets like to sing?

Neptunes!

What is normal eyesight for an alien?

20/20/20!

21

How can you make your money go far?

Put your piggy bank in a rocket!

What's the moon's favorite coin?

Quarters!

Why is the moon bald?

Because it has no 'air!

What starts to work only after it is fired?

A rocket!

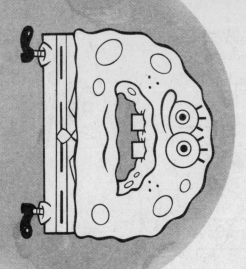

What is at the end of the world?

The letter "D"!

What kind of astronaut can jump higher than a house?

All of them. Houses can't jump!

Why do astronauts like to do subtraction?

They're always ready to count down!

What is the center of gravity?

The letter "V"!

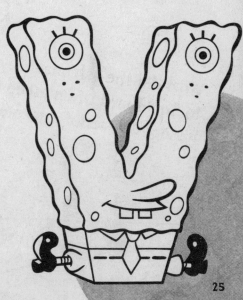

What did the astronaut say to Squidward when asked for his opinion about asteroids?

"No comet!"

What do you call a wizard in space?

A flying saucer-er!

What is an alien's favorite sport?

Spaceball!

How do you make a baby sleep on a space ship?

You rocket!

What are black holes?

What you get in black socks!

How does the man on
the moon cut his hair?

Eclipse it!

What holds up the moon?

Moonbeams!

Where do astronauts keep their sandwiches?

In a launch box!

Why did the astronaut sleep next to a ruler?

To see how long he could sleep!

What is the moon worth?

One dollar, because it has
four quarters!

How do you know when the moon
is going broke?

When it's down to its last quarter!

What should we do when we get dirty in outer space?

Take a meteor shower!

What is an astronaut's favorite
key on the computer keyboard?

The space bar!

What did the astronomer say when
you asked him how he was doing?

"Things are looking up!"

What is a cow's favorite galaxy?

The Milky Way!

Where do aliens keep
their armies?

In their sleevies!

How do you know when the moon isn't hungry?

When it's full!

Why did the astronaut go to bed so close to the sun?

He was a light sleeper!

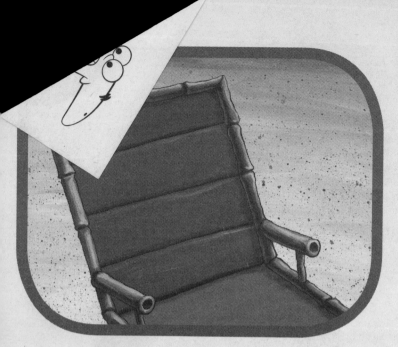

Knock, Knock!

Who's there?

Martian.

Martian who?

I've been martian all day and I really need to sit down!

What's an astronaut's favorite cheese?

Moonster!

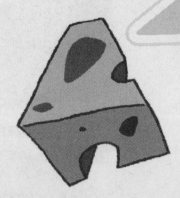

What happens whenever Saturn takes a bath?

It always leaves a ring around the tub!

Why do you never have to wait in line in outer space?

Because you're wait-less!

What did the astronaut see when he was cooking?

Unidentified frying objects.

What's an astronaut's favorite drink?

Gravi-tea.

Did you hear the story about the alien?

It was out of this world!

$$f(x) = \lim_{x \to \infty} \pm\sqrt{\frac{(x^2+x)^3}{\pi}}$$

Why doesn't the sun need to go to college?

Because it already has a thousand degrees!

Where do astronauts leave
their spaceships?

At parking meteors!

What kind of candy
do Martians like?

Mars Bars, of course!

What do you call a funny
space show?

A comet-y!

Why are the moon and Earth good friends?

Because they have been going around together for years!

What did the alien
firefighter say to the
Earth firefighter?

Take me to your ladder.

What do astronauts
wear to bed?

Space jammies!

What type of martial
arts do aliens practice?

Pluto judo!

How do you make a
root beer float?

Send it into outer space!

What does an astronaut use to eat his soup?

A moon spoon!

Did you hear the one about the sun?

It's pretty hot stuff!

Which planet had to go to the cleaners?

Saturn, because it had ring around the collar.

What did the alien say to the librarian?

Take me to your reader!

What is Plankton's favorite drink in outer space?

Ginger-alien!

Where does an alien go to school?

Universe-ity!

What kind of fruit do you eat in outer space?

Star fruit!

Here's a list of books to read before launching into outer space:

When Shall We Meet Again?
by Miles A. Part

A Boy's Trip to Outer Space
by Will Takeoff

How to Call for Assistance in Outer Space
by Linda Hand

Snacks for Astronauts
by San Widge

Still on Earth
by Anita Ride

On the Moon
by I. Malone

Spacewalking
by Hugo Furst